WEIRDOS FROM ANOTHER PLANET!

A Calvin and Hobbes Collection by Bill Watterson

Andrews McMeel
Publishing, LLC

Kansas City • Sydney • London

Calvin and Hobbes is distributed internationally by Universal Uclick.

Weirdos from Another Planet! copyright © 1990 by Bill Watterson.

Andrews McMeel Publishing, LLC
an Andrews McMeel Universal company
1130 Walnut Street, Kansas City, Missouri 64106

www.andrewsmcmeel.com

ISBN: 978-1-4494-0710-0

13 14 15 16 17 SDB 10 9 8 7 6 5

This 2013 edition printed for Barnes & Noble, Inc.

Other Books by Bill Watterson
Calvin and Hobbes
Something Under the Bed is Drooling
Yukon Ho!
The Revenge of the Baby-Sat
Scientific Progress Goes "Boink"
Attack of the Deranged Mutant Killer Monster Snow Goons
The Days Are Just Packed
Homicidal Psycho Jungle Cat

Treasury Collections
The Essential Calvin and Hobbes
The Calvin and Hobbes Lazy Sunday Book
The Authoritative Calvin and Hobbes
The Indispensable Calvin and Hobbes

COME IN, ROSALYN! I'M SORRY! WE DIDN'T REALIZE CALVIN HADN'T LET YOU IN.

THAT'S OK. IT WASN'T *TOO* COLD AND WET OUT.

WE'RE LATE. HELP YOURSELF TO ANYTHING IN THE FRIDGE. WE'LL SEE YOU AT TEN.

THE DOOR WAS JAMMED. REALLY. I COULDN'T GET IT OPEN.

BED.

HEY, DON'T FIX *THAT* FOR DINNER! DIDN'T MOM TELL YOU HOBBES AND I ARE ON A STRICT BIG MAC DIET? IT'S DOCTOR'S ORDERS!

OH, I'D BETTER CALL YOUR DOCTOR THEN!

OH, NO, SHE CALLED MY BLUFF! THE DOCTOR'S GONNA BE FURIOUS! BOY, ARE WE GOING TO GET IT!

"WE"?

I'M DIALING!

HELLO, DOCTOR? I'M CALLING ABOUT CALVIN'S DIETARY NEEDS.

..AT THE TONE, THE TIME WILL BE 6:27 AND 10 SECONDS.
BEEP

BAD NEWS, CALVIN. YOUR DOCTOR SAYS YOU SHOULD HAVE A SPOONFUL OF CASTOR OIL AND LIE DOWN ALL EVENING.

HE DID? REALLY? NO, HE DIDN'T. DID HE? WHAT'S CASTOR OIL?

MOM DOESN'T SET THE TABLE THIS WAY. MOM DOES IT A LOT BETTER.

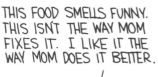

THIS FOOD SMELLS FUNNY. THIS ISN'T THE WAY MOM FIXES IT. I LIKE IT THE WAY MOM DOES IT BETTER.

I'M NOT YOUR MOM, ALL RIGHT?!?

NO KIDDING! MY MOM LOVES ME MORE THAN LIFE ITSELF, AND SHE LETS ME DO ANYTHING I WANT. NOT LIKE *YOU*, YOU NASTY OL' BARRACUDA.

I CAN'T BELIEVE I POSTPONED A DATE FOR THIS.

7

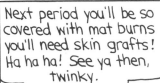

Hey, Calvin, guess what we're doing in gym today. We're wrestling!

Next period you'll be so covered with mat burns you'll need skin grafts! Ha ha ha! See ya then, twinky.

SIGHHHHH....

PHYSICAL EDUCATION IS WHAT YOU LEARN FROM HAVING YOUR FACE IN SOMEONE'S ARMPIT RIGHT BEFORE LUNCH.

KAPWIINGGG! IT'S CALVIN, THE HUMAN LIGHT PARTICLE!

IN THE BLINK OF AN EYE, HE'S 165,000 MILES AWAY!

NOTHING IN THE UNIVERSE IS FASTER THAN CALVIN!

...I HOPE!

MUCH AS I LOVE MY "CHOCOLATE FROSTED CRUNCHY SUGAR BOMBS," THE BEST PART IS AFTER THE CEREAL IS GONE.

THAT'S WHEN YOU EAT THE LEFTOVER MILK THAT'S ALL SLUDGY FROM THE EXTRA SUGAR YOU ADDED.

SOMETIMES I EAT TWO OR THREE BOWLS OF THIS.

I CAN HEAR YOUR HEART RACING FROM HERE.

THEY MAKE THIS CEREAL WITH MARSHMALLOW BITS, TOO, BUT MOM WON'T BUY IT FOR ME.

WHAT'S YOUR TAIL FOR?

MY TAIL?

YEAH. WHY DO TIGERS NEED TAILS?

GEE, I'M NOT REALLY SURE.

I GUESS JUST BECAUSE THEY LOOK GOOD.

SO IT'S SORT OF A NECKTIE FOR YOUR BUTT?

LET'S NOT BE VULGAR. YOU'RE JUST JEALOUS.

I THINK RITUALS ARE IMPORTANT.

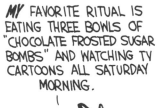

MY FAVORITE RITUAL IS EATING THREE BOWLS OF "CHOCOLATE FROSTED SUGAR BOMBS" AND WATCHING TV CARTOONS ALL SATURDAY MORNING.

AFTER A FEW HOURS, I'M SO OVERSTIMULATED I CAN'T SIT STILL OR EVEN THINK STRAIGHT.

SORT OF A TRANSCENDENTAL EXPERIENCE, HUH?

YEAH. I ACHIEVE A LOWER CONSCIOUSNESS.

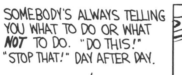

GEE, I'M GETTING MORE LIKE A TIGER EVERY MINUTE.

HOLD STILL WHILE I DRAW STRIPES.

HOW DO I LOOK?

IT'S SOME IMPROVEMENT.

ROWRR RRGHGH RAWRR

I DUNNO, YOU'RE STILL LACKING SOMETHING TIGER-ISH.

PANACHE. THAT'S IT.

WAIT, I'VE GOT SOME PLASTIC VAMPIRE FANGS I CAN PUT IN!

THAT'S GREAT, HOBBES! I'M A TIGER!

WELL, BEING A TIGER IS MORE THAN JUST STRIPES, YOU REALIZE.

KIND OF A ZEN THING, HUH?

YOU HAVE TO THINK LIKE A TIGER.

"YOWWOW, I'M HUNGRY! WHAT'S FOR DINNER?"

... HOW'S THAT?

HAR HAR. DO YOU WANT ME TO TEACH YOU ANYTHING, OR NOT?

OK, WE'RE TIGERS. WE'RE OUT IN THE WILDERNESS. TEACH ME HOW TO SURVIVE.

LET'S SAY WE'RE HIDING UP IN A TREE. OUR KEEN TIGER EYES AND NOSES DETECT SOME PREY NEARBY. WHAT DO WE DO?

I SUPPOSE IT WOULD DEPEND ON WHAT KIND OF PREY IT WAS.

I DON'T CARE. PICK SOMETHING.

WELL, IF IT'S A BOX OF RIGATONI NOODLES, FIRST YOU WOULD GO PUT ON SOME WATER ...

MY SIDE OF THE WOODS ABOUNDS IN NATURAL SCENIC SPLENDOR.

YOUR SIDE WALLOWS IN DECAY AND FILTH. MY TERRITORY IS INFINITELY SUPERIOR TO YOURS.

YOUR SIDE IS SMALLER.

HEY!

I'M HUNGRY.

WELL, YOU CAN'T CATCH ANYTHING IN **MY** TERRITORY. THAT'S WHAT THE BOOK SAYS.

WHAT DO TIGERS EAT IN THE WILD ANYWAY?

THEY CATCH BIG GROSS CATERPILLARS LIKE THAT ONE.

EWWW. IT'S GOT LITTLE SPIKES ALL OVER HIM. TIGERS REALLY EAT THESE?

BY THE TRUCK LOAD. THEY'RE GREAT.

LET ME SEE THE BOOK.

WHO ARE YOU GOING TO BELIEVE, SOME SILLY WRITER OR A REAL TIGER?

SO FAR, I HAVEN'T HAD MUCH FUN AS A TIGER.

I THOUGHT WE'D BE ROMPING AROUND THE WOODS LIKE WE ALWAYS DO, BUT IT TURNS OUT TIGERS DON'T SHARE THEIR TERRITORIES WITH OTHER TIGERS!

SO HERE WE ARE, SITTING ON OPPOSITE SIDES OF A BIG ROCK. WHAT A BLAST.

BEING A TIGER JUST ISN'T ALL IT'S CRACKED UP TO BE.

THAT'S NOT THE HALF OF IT. IT SAYS HERE WE'RE AN ENDANGERED SPECIES!

CALVIN and HOBBES

THE LATE CRETACEOUS PERIOD... WHEN DINOSAURS RULED THE EARTH!

by WATTERSON

..AND CALVIN RULED THE DINOSAURS!

THE TERRIBLE TYRANNOSAURUS SINKS ITS TEETH INTO A TRICERATOPS!

TRIUMPHANT AGAIN, THE UNDISPUTED KING OF DINOSAURS LETS OUT A MIGHTY ROAR!

WITH SAVAGE FEROCITY, THE MONSTER BEGINS ITS FEAST! LIMB-SEVERING, BONE-CRUNCHING AND TENDON-SNAPPING, HE...

CALVIN! THAT'S DISGUSTING!

FOR HEAVEN'S SAKE, SLOW DOWN AND CHEW QUIETLY!

THE TERRIBLE TYRANNOSAURUS RESUMES EATING, MORTIFIED THAT SOMEONE MIGHT SEE HIM.

18

LIGHTNING FLASHES! THUNDER RUMBLES ACROSS THE SKY!

HORRIBLY, CALVIN HAS BEEN SEWN TOGETHER FROM CORPSES! A POWER SURGE FORCES BLOOD TO HIS BRAIN!

HE'S... HE'S *ALIVE!*

WELL, LOOK WHO'S UP AND ABOUT.

HELLO, SLEEPYHEAD.

.OGGG...

CALVIN WAKES UP STARING INTO THE EYES OF A BIG FROG.

SEEING CALVIN AWAKE, THE FROG SCRAMBLES DOWN AND FORCES OPEN CALVIN'S MOUTH!

CALVIN TRIES TO FIGHT, BUT THE SLIPPERY AMPHIBIAN INSTANTLY SLIDES IN AND IS SWALLOWED! HOW DISGUSTING!

I DON'T FEEL GOOD.

YOU SOUND AWFUL. YOU'VE GOT A FROG IN YOUR THROAT.

CALVIN THE ELEPHANT WANDERS THE AFRICAN PLAIN.

AT FIVE TONS, HE IS THE LARGEST LAND MAMMAL!

HIS DEAFENING CALL SHATTERS THE EARLY-MORNING TRANQUILITY!

CALVIN AND HOBBES by WATTERSON

UH OH, I'LL BET HOBBES IS WAITING TO SPRING ON ME AS SOON AS I OPEN THE FRONT DOOR!

I KNOW! I'LL SNEAK AROUND BACK AND SURPRISE *HIM*!

HEH HEH! THERE HE IS, ALL READY TO POUNCE! WHAT A SUCKER!

I'M HOME!

I'VE GOT TO START LISTENING TO THOSE QUIET, NAGGING DOUBTS.

AHH! LUNCH, MY FAVORITE MEAL! AND TODAY'S LUNCH IS *EXTRA* SPECIAL!

EVER SINCE THE WEATHER GOT WARM I'VE BEEN SWATTING FLIES AND SAVING THEM IN A JAR.

FINALLY I GOT ENOUGH BUGS TO MASH THEM INTO A GOOEY PASTE WITH A SPOON.

I CALL IT "BUG BUTTER." CARE FOR A TASTE?

TELL ME, CALVIN, DO YOU HAVE ANY FRIENDS AT *ALL*?

OK, YOU'VE ALL READ THE CHAPTER, SO WHO CAN TELL ME WHAT'S IMPORTANT ABOUT THE BATTLE OF LEXINGTON?

ANYONE?

CALVIN, HOW ABOUT YOU?

HARD TO SAY, MA'AM. I THINK MY CEREBELLUM JUST FUSED.

HEY, MOM, CAN WE GO OUT FOR HAMBURGERS TONIGHT?

NOT TONIGHT, DEAR.

AW, MOM! WHY NOT?

BECAUSE I'M ALREADY FIXING SOMETHING FOR DINNER.

YEAH... I KNOW.

WHY DOES THE SUN SET?

IT'S BECAUSE HOT AIR RISES. THE SUN'S HOT IN THE MIDDLE OF THE DAY, SO IT RISES HIGH IN THE SKY.

IN THE EVENING THEN, IT COOLS DOWN AND SETS.

WHY DOES IT GO FROM EAST TO WEST?

SOLAR WIND.

DEAR!

I'M THINKING OF A NUMBER BETWEEN ONE AND SEVEN HUNDRED BILLION. TRY TO GUESS IT.

ELEVEN?

NOPE. GUESS AGAIN.

SIX MILLION AND FOUR.

NOPE. GUESS AGAIN.

WHAT'S THE MATTER, DON'T YOU LIKE GAMES??

DO YOU BELIEVE OUR DESTINIES ARE DETERMINED BY THE STARS?

NAH.

OH, I DO.

REALLY? HOW COME?

LIFE'S A LOT MORE FUN WHEN YOU'RE NOT RESPONSIBLE FOR YOUR ACTIONS.

CALVIN and HOBBES

by WATERSON

DESPITE THAT AMAZING DISPLAY OF CUNNING, REFLEX AND PHYSICAL PROWESS, YOUR TAIL STILL HAS A DEATH GRIP ON YOUR BUTT.

COULD YOU STOP THE ROOM, PLEASE? I'D LIKE TO GET OFF.

EIGHT... NINE... TEN! HERE I COME, READY OR NOT!

ALL RIGHT, GIVE 'EM BACK!

CALVIN, I'D LIKE YOU TO PICK UP ALL THE STICKS AND FALLEN BRANCHES IN THE YARD, SO I CAN MOW IT.

WILL YOU PAY ME?

WELL... OK, I'LL PAY YOU A DOLLAR.

A DOLLAR? I WON'T DO IT FOR LESS THAN TWENTY-FIVE!!

IN A MINUTE YOU'LL DO IT FOR NOTHING, JUST BECAUSE I TOLD YOU TO.

..I'LL TAKE THE DOLLAR.

SMART KID.

OK, OUT OF THE HAMMOCK.

WHAT DO YOU MEAN? THIS ISN'T YOUR HAMMOCK.

IT'S MY TURN.

I WAS HERE FIRST. IT'S YOUR TURN WHEN I'M DONE.

IF YOU WON'T GET OUT, THEN I'M COMING IN WITH YOU.

LIKE HECK YOU ARE!

THIS CRUMMY HAMMOCK ALWAYS SAGS.

BAD NEWS ON YOUR POLLS, DAD. YOU DROPPED ANOTHER FIVE POINTS.

IT SEEMS THAT ALTHOUGH YOUR RECOGNITION FACTOR IS HIGH, THE SCANDALS OF YOUR ADMINISTRATION CONTINUE TO HAUNT YOU.

SCANDALS? WHAT SCANDALS?!

BEDTIMEGATE AND HOMEWORKGATE COME READILY TO MIND.

INSTANCES OF TRUE LEADERSHIP. HISTORY WILL VINDICATE ME.

I WONDER WHAT MY NEW DAD WILL LOOK LIKE.

YOU'LL BE GLAD TO KNOW I'VE ANALYZED YOUR POOR SHOWING IN THE POLLS.

I'LL BET.

SEE, YOUR RECORD IN OFFICE IS MISERABLE AND THE CHARACTER ISSUE IS KILLING YOU. YOUR BASIC APPROVAL RATING AMONG SIX-YEAR-OLDS HARDLY REGISTERS.

IF ANYONE EVER NEEDED A SLICK AD CAMPAIGN, IT'S YOU.

LET ME GUESS WHAT YOU HAVE IN MIND.

"THE *NEW* DAD" I CALL IT.

I THINK THE IMAGE WE NEED TO CREATE FOR YOU IS, "REPENTANT, BUT LEARNING."

YOU KNOW, SHOW SOME HUMILITY, AND PRESENT YOURSELF AS A REGULAR GUY TRYING TO LEARN THE ROPES OF A DIFFICULT JOB.

DIFFICULT DOESN'T BEGIN TO DESCRIBE IT.

I WORKED UP SOME SLOGANS. SEE WHAT YOU THINK.

**"DAD—GRADUALLY, HE CATCHES ON."
"VOTE DAD! *THIS* TIME, HE'LL DO BETTER."
"TO FORGIVE IS DIVINE—VOTE DAD IN '88."**

I GET THE IDEA, CALVIN.

IF YOU WANT TO STAY DAD, YOU'VE GOT TO POLISH YOUR IMAGE.

MY IMAGE.

RIGHT. SEE, NOW EVERYONE THINKS YOU'RE INSENSITIVE TO THE LEGITIMATE NEEDS OF MINORS.

A FEW MAGNANIMOUS GESTURES WHILE IN OFFICE NOW MIGHT BE IN ORDER. IF YOUR MIND'S GONE BLANK, I HAVE SOME SUGGESTIONS.

OH, THE SUSPENSE.

FOR EXAMPLE, YOU MIGHT REPEAL MANDATORY SCHOOL ATTENDANCE. THAT ALONE COULD ROCKET YOU TO VICTORY.

MUCH AS I APPRECIATE YOUR OFFER, I DON'T THINK I NEED AN IMAGE CONSULTANT.

I PREFER TO LET THE WISDOM OF MY WORDS AND DEEDS SPEAK FOR THEMSELVES.

IN THAT CASE, YOU'LL HAVE A LOT OF TIME TO WRITE YOUR MEMOIRS.

WE'LL SEE. NOW IT'S PAST YOUR BEDTIME.

"DAD BURIED IN LANDSLIDE! JUBILANT THRONGS FILL STREETS! STUNNED FATHER INCONSOLABLE — DEMANDS RECOUNT!"

GOOD NIGHT.

calvin and HobbEs

by WATTERSON

YES, YOU CAN CERTAINLY SEE FAR FROM UP HERE.

I CALL THIS "LOOKOUT" HILL.

I CALL IT "LOOKOUT" HILL BECAUSE THAT'S WHAT YOU YELL WHENEVER WE GO DOWN IT.

YOU KNOW, SOMETIMES IT SEEMS THINGS GO BY TOO QUICKLY.

WE'RE SO BUSY WATCHING OUT FOR WHAT'S JUST AHEAD OF US THAT WE DON'T TAKE THE TIME TO ENJOY WHERE WE ARE.

DAYS GO BY AND WE HARDLY NOTICE THEM. LIFE BECOMES A BLUR.

OFTEN IT TAKES SOME CALAMITY TO MAKE US LIVE IN THE PRESENT.

THEN SUDDENLY WE WAKE UP AND SEE ALL THE MISTAKES WE'VE MADE, BUT IT'S TOO LATE TO CHANGE ANYTHING.

IT'S LIKE... ...IT'S LIKE...

IT'S LIKE WHAT?

IT'S LIKE *SOME*THING... I JUST CAN'T THINK OF IT.

NUTS! THIS WHEEL STRUT SNAPPED. WHY DO THEY MAKE 'EM SO DARN SMALL?

I GUESS THAT WAS AN OPTIONAL PIECE.

MY WHEEL WON'T FIT IN THE WHEEL WELL.

HERE, LET ME TRY. SOMETIMES YOU JUST HAVE TO...

SNAP

DARN IT!

THIS PLANE IS IN FOR SOME ROUGH LANDINGS.

LOOK AT THIS STUPID MODEL. IT LOOKS AWFUL!

OUR PLANE DOESN'T LOOK ANYTHING LIKE THE PICTURE ON THE BOX.

MAYBE WE CAN FIX IT WHEN WE PAINT IT.

I CAN'T PAINT IT LIKE THIS. LOOK HOW GOOD THEY DID THIS!

HOW'D THEY PAINT EYEBROWS ON A PILOT THAT'S LESS THAN AN INCH TALL ??

I THINK THAT'S A REAL JET SUPERIMPOSED ON A PLASTIC STAND.

I HATE THIS MODEL. NOTHING FIT RIGHT, THE INSTRUCTIONS WERE INCOMPREHENSIBLE, THE DECALS RIPPED, THE PAINT SLOPPED, AND THE GLUE GOT EVERYWHERE.

WHAT A DISASTER. SIX BUCKS COMPLETELY DOWN THE DRAIN.

I CAN'T THINK OF AN AFTERNOON I'VE ENJOYED LESS. WHAT A WASTE. WHAT A DUMB HOBBY.

..OF COURSE, WITH THIS FOR PRACTICE, I'LL BET WE COULD DO GREAT ON ANOTHER MODEL!

LET'S GET ONE OF THOSE CLIPPER SHIPS WITH ALL THE RIGGINGS.

Calvin and Hobbes
by WATTERSON

A VOICE CACKLES IN CALVIN'S RADIO. "ENEMY FIGHTERS AT TWO O'CLOCK!"

ROGER. WHAT SHOULD I DO UNTIL THEN?

CALVIN'S F-4 PHANTOM SCREAMS ACROSS THE SKY!

BUT WHAT'S THIS? THE CANOPY GLASS IS ALL SMEARED! HE CAN HARDLY SEE THROUGH IT!

OH, NO! THE THROTTLE SNAPS OFF IN HIS HAND!

CALVIN'S ONLY HOPE IS TO LAND, BUT THE WHEELS REFUSE TO OPEN! THEY'RE STUCK!

FRANTICALLY CALVIN TRIES TO EJECT, BUT THE COCKPIT IS FUSED TOGETHER! HIS JET IS A HOPELESS MESS! EVERYTHING IS GOING WRONG!

STUPID MODEL.

I'M NOT GOING TO BED! I DON'T HAVE TO DO WHAT YOU SAY! I CAN DO ANYTHING I WANT!

..UH.. HEH HEH

ENJOY THIS WHILE YOU CAN! I'LL BE A HULKING, SURLY TEEN-AGER BEFORE YOU KNOW IT!!

DID YOU EVER WONDER IF THE PERSON IN THE PUDDLE IS REAL, AND YOU'RE JUST A REFLECTION OF HIM?

IF THAT WAS TRUE, YOU'D DISAPPEAR AS SOON AS THE PERSON IN THE PUDDLE MOVED AWAY FROM THE PUDDLE, RIGHT?

GEE, I GUESS SO. I HADN'T THOUGHT OF THAT.

BANG!

BANG! BANG!

HA! THAT'S SIX SHOTS! YOU'RE OUT OF BULLETS! I'VE GOT YOU NOW, YOU RUSTLER!

ZAP!

"ZAP"?

MY CATTLE PROD.

HEY, SUSIE, GUESS WHAT I HAVE IN MY HANDS!

IS IT DISGUSTING?

UM... ..WELL...

IS IT SOME CREEPY, GOOEY THING THAT NO ONE IN HIS RIGHT MIND WOULD EVER, EVER WANT TO LOOK AT?

UH... I. SUPPOSE THAT DEPENDS ON YOUR POINT OF VIEW...

FORGET IT. I'M NOT GUESSING.

YOU MIGHT AS WELL. YOU'RE NINE-TENTHS THERE.

MOM, WAS I EVER A GRUB?

A WHAT?

YOU KNOW, A LARVA. DID I REALLY PUPATE AT AGE TWO?

DON'T BE DISGUSTING! OF COURSE NOT! WHERE DID YOU EVER GET THAT AWFUL IDEA?!

YOU SHOULD GET YOUR STORIES STRAIGHT WITH MOM, MR. BRITANNICA!

HOW CAN YOU STAND THESE CARTOONS?

THEY'RE JUST HALF-HOUR COMMERCIALS FOR TOYS. AND WHEN THEY'RE NOT BORING, THEY'RE PREACHY.

AND THESE CHARACTERS DON'T EVEN *MOVE*. THEY JUST STAND AROUND BLINKING! WHAT KIND OF CARTOON IS *THAT*?

MEET MY DAD, THE GENE SISKEL OF SATURDAY MORNING TV.

Calvin and Hobbes

by WATTERSON

C'MON, HOBBES. LET ME UP INTO THE TREE FORT.

SAY THE PASSWORD.

NO! YOU KNOW IT'S ME! LET ME UP!

YOU MAY BE SOME OTHER KID IN DISGUISE.

IT'S *ME*, CALVIN! LET ME UP, YOU HAIRBALL BARFER!

AN INSULT! WELL, YOU CAN JUST STAY DOWN THERE *FOREVER*, MR. STINKER.

OH, NO! HERE COMES SUSIE! LET ME UP QUICK, SO WE CAN THROW THINGS AT HER! HURRY! LET DOWN THE ROPE!

LA DE DA DUM DOO ♪♫

SHE'S COMING! QUICK! LET DOWN THE ROPE! I'M SORRY I INSULTED YOU! OK? SEE, I SAID I WAS SORRY! CAN'T YOU LET DOWN THE ROPE?!

YOU HAVE TO SAY THE PASSWORD.

..Verse Seven: TIGERS ARE PERFECT, THE *E*-PIT-O-ME OF GOOD LOOKS AND GRACE AND QUIET..UH..UM..DIGNITY.

I WAS GOING TO ASK YOU TO COME OVER AND PLAY HOUSE, BUT I THINK YOU'D BE A WEIRD EXAMPLE FOR OUR CHILDREN.

ONE OF THESE DAYS I'M GOING TO MAKE YOU INTO A RUG! YOU HEAR ME?? A <u>RUG</u>!

CAN I USE THE GARDEN SHOVEL?

WHAT DO YOU WANT IT FOR?

HOBBES AND I ARE GOING ON AN ARCHAEOLOGICAL EXPEDITION.

IF YOU'RE LOOKING FOR FOSSILIZED REMAINS, YOU SHOULD DIG THROUGH YOUR ROOM.

HA HA. SOMEDAY I'LL NAME AN AUSTRALOPITHECUS WOMAN AFTER YOU.

I'VE BEEN READING UP ON PALEONTOLOGY. IT'S AMAZING STUFF.

SCIENTISTS CAN TELL HOW OLD SOMETHING IS JUST BY ANALYZING THE LAYERS OF DIRT IT'S IN.

HEY!

WHY, YOU MUST BE SIX YEARS OLD.

OH, YOU'RE A SCREAM.

ARCHAEOLOGISTS DIG SLOWLY AND CAREFULLY, USING SMALL, DELICATE TOOLS.

EACH ROCK HAS TO BE PAINSTAKINGLY BRUSHED AND SCRAPED SO NOTHING IS BROKEN OR MISSED.

DIG DIG SCRAPE SCRAPE BRUSH BRUSH

ARCHAEOLOGISTS HAVE THE MOST MIND-NUMBING JOB ON THE PLANET.

I DON'T THINK YOUR DAD WILL WANT TO SHAVE WITH THIS TOMORROW.

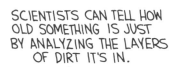

GOSH, LOOK AT ALL THE DINOSAUR BONES WE DISCOVERED.

LET'S GLUE THEM TOGETHER SO WE CAN SEE HOW THEY FIT. THEN YOU CAN DRAW A RECONSTRUCTION OF THE ACTUAL DINOSAUR.

AFTER THAT, WE'LL WRITE UP OUR FINDINGS, AND GET THEM PUBLISHED IN A SCIENTIFIC JOURNAL.

THEN WE'LL WIN THE NOBEL PRIZE, GET RICH, AND GO ON TALK SHOWS.

WHAT ABOUT BABES? WHEN DO WE GET THOSE?

WELL, HERE'S THE COMPLETE SKELETON AS NEAR AS *I* CAN FIGURE OUT.

TRY TO DRAW THE DINOSAUR AS IT REALLY LOOKED WITH MUSCLES AND SKIN.

RIGHT.

WHAT'S IT DOING? WHISTLING?

YOU TELL ME. MAYBE IT'S PUCKERING UP.

SEE THE DINOSAUR SKELETON WE DISCOVERED AND ASSEMBLED?

I'M GOING TO CALL THE NATURAL HISTORY MUSEUM AND TELL THEM THEY CAN HAVE IT FOR TEN BILLION DOLLARS.

THOSE ARE ..UM... PECULIAR BONES.

DO YOU THINK I SHOULD ASK FOR MORE MONEY?

THAT'S NOT *QUITE* WHAT I MEANT.

 MOM SAYS SHE DOESN'T THINK WE'VE FOUND A SKELETON AT ALL.

 SHE SAYS WE JUST DUG UP SOME TRASH SOMEBODY LITTERED.

 OUR DINOSAUR IS A FRAUD.

 I GUESS IT WOULDN'T BE RIGHT TO SELL IT TO A MUSEUM THEN.

NOT AT FULL PRICE, ANYWAY.

 PSST...SUSIE! CAN I COPY YOUR PAPER?

NO.

 CALVIN!

 AAUGHH! I SKINNED MY KNEE! OOH! OW!

 AAUGHHH! OW! OW!

40

Calvin and Hobbes

by WATTERSON

THE CALL GOES OUT! WE'RE ON THE MOVE!

UP THROUGH THE WINDING MAZE! FASTER! FASTER!

CALVIN SCRAMBLES UP THE GRAINY TUNNEL!

OUT HE POPS INTO THE BLINDING SUN! CALVIN THE ANT RUSHES DOWN THE HILL TO THE BRICK WALK!

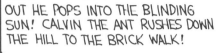

OTHER ANTS RUSH AROUND HIM IN THEIR MAD HURRY! CALVIN TRIES TO KEEP UP!

AT LAST HE REACHES THE MONSTROUS DEAD CATERPILLAR! WITHOUT PAUSING, HE HOISTS IT UP!

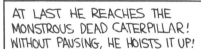

THE QUEEN DEMANDS HIS TIRELESS TOIL! CALVIN IS BACK OFF TO THE ANT-HILL AS FAST AS HE CAN GO!

WORK, WORK, WORK! THAT'S ALL I'M GOOD FOR AROUND HERE!

I HARDLY THINK PICKING UP YOUR ROOM ONCE IN A WHILE QUALIFIES YOU AS A SLAVE.

CaLViN and HobbES

by WATTERSON

THIS IS CALVIN, YOUR CAPTAIN, SPEAKING...

...JUST TO REASSURE YOU THAT, YES, THERE IS SOMEONE UP FRONT.

CALVIN PILOTS THE JET AIRLINER ACROSS THE COUNTRY AT 35,000 FEET.

HE IS GIVEN CLEARANCE TO LAND. BUT WHAT'S THIS? A PLANE FROM A RIVAL AIRLINE IS MAKING FOR THE SAME RUNWAY TO SHAVE PRECIOUS MINUTES OFF ITS SCHEDULE!

IT'S A 600-MPH GAME OF CHICKEN! CALVIN PULLS BACK ON THE THROTTLE AND LURCHES AHEAD!

THE OTHER PILOT TRIES TO CUT CALVIN OFF WITH A SUDDEN DROP IN ALTITUDE!

CALVIN SWITCHES ON THE "FASTEN SEAT BELT" LIGHT IN THE CABIN, AND DOES A BARREL ROLL!

AT 5 Gs, CALVIN HOPES NOT TO BLACK OUT!

AS THEY CLOSE IN ON THE RUNWAY, THE OTHER PILOT HAS NO CHOICE BUT TO PULL UP AND CIRCLE AROUND AGAIN! CALVIN WINS!

HEY, MOM, IS IT TRUE I COULD GET A PILOT'S LICENSE AT AGE 14?

NO.

I HAD NO *IDEA* BINOCULARS WERE SO EXPENSIVE! WE'RE DOOMED! WE'RE DOOMED!

"WE"?

WHY IN THE WORLD DID DAD LET ME USE ANYTHING SO VALUABLE?! HE SHOULD'VE *KNOWN* I'D BREAK THEM! HE MUST'VE BEEN OUT OF HIS MIND! THIS IS ALL *HIS* FAULT!

WHAT AM I GONNA *DO*?!

I SUPPOSE YOU *COULD* JUST TELL HIM WHAT HAPPENED...

..AND MAKE MY GETAWAY WHEN THE CORONARY HITS? SAY, *THAT'S* AN IDEA!

MAYBE WE COULD *GLUE* DAD'S BINOCULARS BACK TOGETHER AND HE WOULDN'T EVEN NOTICE! YOU THINK?

IT DEPENDS. WAS THE CASING JUST CHIPPED A LITTLE, OR DID THE LENS ITSELF GET CRACKED?

WELL, MAYBE YOU'D BETTER LOOK AT IT.

DON'T SNEEZE.

MAYBE YOU SHOULD TELL YOUR *MOM* ABOUT THE BINOCULARS, AND SHE CAN HELP SOMEHOW.

TELL MOM?!? ARE YOU CRAZY?? NO WAY!

WHY NOT? YOU'VE GOT TO TELL *SOMEONE*. MAYBE SHE CAN THINK OF SOMETHING.

AT TIMES LIKE THESE, ALL MOM CAN THINK OF IS HOW LONG SHE WAS IN LABOR WITH ME.

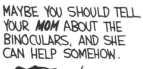

LOOK AT DAD, CALMLY EATING HIS DINNER AS IF NOTHING WAS WRONG.
I KNOW HIM. HIS "DAD RADAR" IS BEEPING LIKE CRAZY. HE KNOWS I BROKE SOMETHING, HE JUST DOESN'T KNOW WHAT. HE CAN'T NAIL ME UNTIL HE KNOWS FOR SURE. HE'LL JUST WAIT. I KNOW HIM.
HE'S GOING TO JUST SIT THERE EATING AND LET ME STEW IN MY OWN GUILT. HE FIGURES SOONER OR LATER I'LL CRACK.
CALVIN?
AAUGH! I DID IT! I DID IT! I'M SORRY! I DIDN'T MEAN TO!!
..PASS THE UH.. ..THE UH...
WATTERSON

YOU BROKE THE BINOCULARS?!
DIDN'T I TELL YOU TO BE EXTRA, EXTRA CAREFUL WITH THEM?? ISN'T THAT EXACTLY WHAT
WELL?!
THOSE BINOCULARS WERE BRAND NEW! HAVE YOU NO RESPECT FOR OTHER PEOPLE'S PROPERTY?!?
I HAVE AN IDEA, DAD. LET'S PRETEND I ALREADY FEEL TERRIBLE ABOUT IT, AND THAT YOU DON'T NEED TO RUB IT IN ANY MORE.
WATTERSON

I DIDN'T MEAN TO BREAK YOUR BINOCULARS, DAD. IT WAS AN ACCIDENT.
(SNIFF) I'M REALLY SORRY. I FELT LIKE I WAS GOING TO BARF ALL AFTERNOON.
WELL, I'M SORRY I YELLED AT YOU LIKE I DID. I SHOULDN'T HAVE BEEN SO ANGRY.
AFTER ALL, IT WAS JUST A PAIR OF BINOCULARS. IN THE BIG SCHEME OF THINGS, THAT'S REALLY NOT SO BAD.
(SNIFF) REALLY?
SURE. ...IN ANOTHER TEN YEARS, YOU'LL PROBABLY BE WRECKING MY CAR.
WATTERSON

HOBBES, LOOK! DAD GOT ME MY OWN PAIR OF LITTLE BINOCULARS!

WOW, THESE ARE *YOURS*?

AREN'T THEY GREAT?

I'LL SAY.

DAD SAID AS LONG AS I WAS GOING TO BREAK BINOCULARS, I OUGHT TO AT LEAST BREAK MY OWN.

NOW WE CAN GO TO THE BEACH AND LOOK AT BABES!

MAYBE I SHOULD BREAK DAD'S POWER TOOLS AND SEE IF I COULD GET SOME OF *THOSE*.

WIND WIND WIND

RUMBLE RUMBLE

EITHER I'M GREATLY DECEIVED, OR SOMEONE OPENED A CAN OF TUNA IN THIS VICINITY!

YES... ALL OVER THIS VICINITY.

WHAT A CLEAR NIGHT! LOOK AT ALL THE STARS. MILLIONS OF THEM!

YES, WE'RE JUST TINY SPECS ON A PLANET PARTICLE, HURLING THROUGH THE INFINITE BLACKNESS.

LET'S GO IN AND TURN ON ALL THE LIGHTS.

CALVIN AND HOBBES by WATTERSON

zzzzzzzzzzzzz

FILTH! CONTAMINATION! PESTILENCE! HA HA HA!

OF ALL LIVING CREATURES, FEW ARE MORE REPULSIVE THAN CALVIN THE BUG!

HE EXISTS ONLY TO SUCK BLOOD AND TRANSMIT PARASITIC DISEASE!

SEARCHING FOR SOMEONE TO INFECT, CALVIN FLIES LOW OVER THE PICNIC TABLE!

INGREDIENTS: SALT,

HIS SENSITIVE ANTENNAE PICK UP THE SCENT OF HUMAN FLESH!

TOUCHING DOWN, CALVIN INSERTS HIS NEEDLELIKE PROBOSCIS INTO A VEIN! PROTOZOANS IN HIS SALIVA QUICKLY INDUCE PLAGUE!

WILL YOU STOP THAT AWFUL SLURPING?! YOU'RE MAKING ME SICK!

48

DON'T MOVE! THERE'S A BEE ON YOUR BACK!

THERE IS?! SHOO IT AWAY! QUICK!

AND HAVE IT COME AFTER *ME*? NO, THANKS.

WELL, WHAT AM I SUPPOSED TO DO? STAND LIKE *THIS* ALL DAY?

I GUESS YOU DON'T HAVE MUCH CHOICE, DO YOU?

GREAT. JUST GREAT. I COULD BE HERE FOREVER!

SAY, THAT GIVES ME AN IDEA.

DON'T YOU GO READING MY COMIC BOOKS! STAY OUT OF MY ROOM!

THAT ROTTEN HOBBES! I CAN'T MOVE BECAUSE I'VE GOT A BEE ON MY BACK, SO HE GOES TO READ ALL MY COMIC BOOKS!

HE ALWAYS GETS THEM OUT OF ORDER, AND HE FOLDS THE COVERS BACK! OOH, IF I COULD ONLY MOVE!

WHAT KIND OF FRIEND WOULD TAKE ADVANTAGE OF A PREDICAMENT LIKE THIS? A LOUSY FRIEND, *THAT'S* WHAT KIND! WHAT A STINKER HE IS!

HEY, DID YOU SEE HOW THE LATEST ISSUE OF CAPTAIN NAPALM ENDED?

DON'T TELL ME! DON'T TELL ME!

HOBBES, IF YOU TELL ME HOW MY COMIC BOOK ENDS, I'LL KILL YOU. I'VE WAITED ALL MONTH TO FIND OUT.

I'LL GIVE YOU A HINT, OK? CAPTAIN NAPALM TAKES HIS NUCLEAR...

NO HINTS! NO HINTS!

BY GOLLY, YOU HAIRBALL, IF I DIDN'T HAVE A BEE ON MY BACK RIGHT NOW, I'D...

MAYBE THERE'S A BEE AND MAYBE THERE ISN'T. *I'LL* NEVER TELL.

WHAT?! IS THE BEE GONE? CAN I MOVE? TELL ME! IS IT STILL THERE?? HUH? RRGGH! IS IT?!

IS THE BEE STILL ON ME OR NOT?

I'M NOT TELLING. YOU CALLED ME A HAIRBALL.

OK, OK, I'M SORRY. YOU'RE NOT A HAIRBALL. NOW, IS THE BEE THERE OR NOT?

NO.

GOOD. NOW I...

I MEANT "NO, THERE IS A BEE." TODAY IS OPPOSITE DAY!

DON'T FORGET... AT MIDNIGHT OPPOSITE DAY IS OVER, OK?

"YES."

I'M NOT HAVING DINNER TONIGHT.

OH NO?

NOPE. I'M JUST GOING TO EAT COOKIES IN FRONT OF THE TV.

YOU, YOUNG MAN, ARE GOING TO SIT AT THE TABLE AND EAT WHAT I'VE FIXED, JUST LIKE THE REST OF US.

OH, YEAH. THAT'S WHAT I MEANT.

HELLO, I'M WONDERING IF YOU SELL KEGS OF DYNAMITE.

YOU DON'T? HOW ABOUT PLASTIC EXPLOSIVES?

YOU'RE KIDDING. WELL, WHAT ABOUT LAND MINES? DO YOU SELL THOSE? ... YOU DON'T?

LOOK, I'M TRYING TO SEND A GIRL I KNOW INTO DEEP SPACE. PERHAPS YOU COULD SUGGEST SOMETHING.

YOU KNOW WHAT WE NEED, HOBBES? WE NEED AN ATTITUDE.

AN ATTITUDE?

YEAH. YOU CAN'T BE COOL IF YOU DON'T HAVE AN ATTITUDE.

REALLY?

SURE. THEY'RE ALL THE RAGE. NOW WHAT KIND OF ATTITUDE COULD *WE* HAVE?

WE COULD BE COURTEOUSLY DEFERENTIAL.

OH, GOOD. THAT'S *REAL* COOL.

I'VE DECIDED TO BE A FATALIST.

ALL EVENTS ARE PREORDAINED AND UNALTERABLE. WHATEVER WILL BE WILL BE. THAT WAY, IF ANYTHING BAD HAPPENS, IT'S NOT MY FAULT. IT'S FATE.

TRIP

WAUGH

TOO BAD YOU WERE FATED TO DO THAT.

THAT WASN'T FATE!

DO YOU THINK GROWN-UPS WILL HAVE THE WORLD FIXED UP BY THE TIME THEY HAND IT OVER TO US?

NOT THE WAY THEY'RE GOING.

THAT'S WHAT *I* THOUGHT.

I GUESS THAT MEANS IT'S UP TO *US* THEN.

SOMEHOW, I'M NOT REASSURED.

HA! WHEN *I'M* PRESIDENT, I'LL HAVE THINGS WHIPPED INTO SHAPE IN NO TIME.

EITHER WE'VE GOT TO GET A CATCHER, OR YOU'VE GOT TO IMPROVE YOUR PITCHING.

GOSH, IT SURE LOOKS LIKE RAIN.

RAIN? WHAT ARE YOU TALKING ABOUT? THERE ISN'T A CLOUD IN THE SKY!

YOU DON'T THINK IT LOOKS LIKE RAIN?

NO. GO AWAY AND STOP BEING SILLY.

HEY, LOOK! MOM AND DAD ARE THROWING DUFFEL BAGS IN THE CAR. THEY'RE GOING ON VACATION!

AT LAST! FINALLY WE GET THE HOUSE TO OURSELVES! WE CAN STAY UP LATE AND WATCH TV! WE CAN EAT COOKIES FOR DINNER! WE...

WHAT ARE YOU DOING UP HERE STILL? C'MON, LET'S GO.

ME? GO? GO WHERE?

ON VACATION! WHAT HAVE WE BEEN PLANNING ALL MONTH?

WITH YOU AND MOM?? WHAT KIND OF VACATION IS *THAT*?!

SO WHERE ARE WE GOING? I SURE HOPE WE'RE NOT CAMPING AGAIN THIS YEAR.

WELL, WE ARE.

OH, NO! WHY DO WE HAVE TO GO CAMPING?! I *HATE* CAMPING!

SWATTING MOSQUITOES WHILE LYING FROZEN AND CRAMPED ON BUMPY ROCKS, WITH NO TV AND ONLY CANNED FOOD TO EAT, IS *NOT* MY IDEA OF A GOOD TIME!

THAT'S WHY WE BROUGHT BUG SPRAY.

LOOK, JUST LET ME OUT HERE, OK? I'LL HITCH HOME AND SEE YOU WHEN YOU GET BACK, ALL RIGHT?

REMEMBER LAST YEAR, WHEN IT RAINED ALL WEEK? IT POURED SO HARD WE COULDN'T EVEN MAKE A FIRE.

WITHOUT QUESTION, THAT WAS ONE OF THE WORST EXPERIENCES OF MY LIFE.

YES, BUT IT BUILT CHARACTER.

OH SURE.

WHY CAN'T I EVER BUILD CHARACTER AT A MIAMI CONDO OR A CASINO SOMEWHERE?

WELL, HERE WE ARE! HOME AWAY FROM HOME!

OK, CALVIN, YOU GET OUT WITH YOUR MOM, AND I'LL HAND OUR GEAR TO YOU.

NOW DON'T DROP THIS. IT'S VERY...

OOPS.

PLOONK

DON'T WORRY, DAD. IT'S ONLY ABOUT TEN FEET DEEP. I CAN SEE THE CAMERA AND EVERYTHING.

I AM GOING TO FEED YOU TO THE SEA GULLS, KID.

DEAR, YOU CAME HERE TO RELAX.

GOSH, THIS WATER'S COLD! HERE, THAT'S ALL I COULD FIND DOWN THERE. GO GET ME A TOWEL, CALVIN.

IT NEVER FAILS. THE ONE BAG THE KID DUMPS IN THE DRINK HAS ALL THE FRAGILE AND PERISHABLE ITEMS IN IT.

WELL, THE WEEK CAN ONLY IMPROVE FROM HERE.

ONE WOULD LIKE TO THINK SO.

HEY, DAD, DID YOU MEAN TO STACK THE TACKLE BOX AND ALL THIS ON YOUR GLASSES?

BOY, DON'T GO NEAR DAD. WHAT A GROUCH!

I DON'T SEE WHY HE CAN'T BE CIVIL JUST BECAUSE I ACCIDENTALLY DROPPED A DUFFEL BAG OVERBOARD AND HE BROKE HIS GLASSES.

ARE YOU GOING TO TELL HIM HE LEFT THE CAR LIGHTS ON BACK WHERE WE GOT THE CANOE?

I THINK YOU SHOULD TELL HIM.

HEY, MOM, DAD AND I ARE GOING FISHING. DON'T YOU WANT TO COME ALONG?

UGGH, NO. THE LAST THING I WANT TO SEE AT THIS UNGODLY HOUR IS A BUNCH OF SLIMY FISH GASPING AND FLOPPING IN THE SLOP AT THE BOTTOM OF A BOAT.

ALL *I'D* LIKE TO SEE IS A DECENT NEWSPAPER, A FRESH MUFFIN AND A POT OF REAL COFFEE.

WHY'D WE EVER COME *HERE* THEN?

GO ASK CONAN THE BARBARIAN.

C'MON, CALVIN. I'LL TEACH YOU TO PUT A WORM ON A HOOK.

AHHH, WHAT A DAY!

UP AT DAWN! FRESH AIR! TRANQUILITY! NO DEMANDS, NO PHONES, NO PRESSURE!

THE WHOLE DAY IS ONE'S OWN! ISN'T THIS GREAT? ISN'T THIS THE LIFE?

SPACEMAN SPIFF, A PRISONER ON THE ZOG SLAVE GALLEY, PLANS HIS DARING OVERBOARD ESCAPE!

AHH, WHAT A DAY!

GOSH, I COULD LOOK AT THE STARS ALL NIGHT.

WITHOUT THE STREETLIGHTS OR POLLUTION HERE, IT SEEMS LIKE YOU CAN SEE FOREVER INTO SPACE.

SNAP CRUNCH

OF COURSE, IF YOU'VE SEEN ONE STAR, YOU'VE SEEN THEM ALL.

TRUE, TRUE. SHALL WE MOSEY ON BACK TO THE TENT?

LOOK, MOM, THE WATER IS UP TO MY KNEES!

SEE? SEE? LOOK, MOM! THE WATER'S UP TO MY KNEES! SEE? LOOK WHERE THE WATER IS!

NOW LOOK! THE WATER IS *HIGHER* THAN MY KNEES! SEE? LOOK, MOM! SEE?

I'M ENTHRALLED, CALVIN.

YOU'RE NOT EVEN LOOKING!

WHATCHA DOIN', DAD? PAINTING A PICTURE?

YEP.

WHAT'S THAT THING? A BRONTOSAURUS WITH RABIES?

IT'S THAT ISLAND OVER THERE.

OH.

HOW FAR CAN YOU SEE WITHOUT YOUR GLASSES? CAN YOU SEE *ME*?

WHEN I LOOK UP, I'D BETTER NOT BE ABLE TO.

HI, MOM!

MM.

DAD'S PAINTING A PICTURE, BUT IT'S NOT COMING OUT SO HOT, AND HE'S IN A REALLY STINKY MOOD. IT'S LIKE, I ASKED HIM ONE LITTLE QUESTION AND HE NEARLY BIT MY HEAD OFF! I MEAN, IT'S NOT AS IF *I* RUINED HIS LOUSY PICTURE, RIGHT? WHY SHOULD...

CALVIN, CAN'T YOU SEE I'M TRYING TO READ?

EVER NOTICE HOW TENSE GROWN-UPS GET WHEN THEY'RE RECREATING?

THERE'S NOTHING TO *DO* HERE.

THAT'S SORT OF THE POINT, DON'T YOU THINK? IT'S GOOD TO STOP RUNNING AROUND.

SOMETIMES ONE SHOULD JUST LOOK AT THINGS AND THINK ABOUT THINGS, WITHOUT *DOING* THINGS.

YOU'RE CERTAINLY THE EXPERT ON *THAT*.

WHAT I LIKE IS WHEN YOU'RE LOOKING AND THINKING AND LOOKING AND THINKING....AND SUDDENLY YOU WAKE UP.

MOM, CAN HOBBES COME IN SWIMMING WITH ME?

I DON'T THINK HE'D BETTER, CALVIN.

WHY NOT?

UM... TIGERS DON'T SWIM VERY WELL.

THEY DON'T?

FRANKLY, I'M NOT SURE YOUR MOM KNOWS SO MUCH ABOUT TIGERS.

LOOK, WE JUST WANT TO AVOID AN ARGUMENT, RIGHT?

OK, CALVIN, START PACKING UP. WE'RE GOING HOME.

FINALLY!

NOW, NOW. THESE LITTLE OUTINGS ARE VALUABLE EXPERIENCES.

YEAH? HOW?

THEY GIVE US A CHANCE TO BE TOGETHER AS A FAMILY AND LEARN ABOUT OURSELVES.

LIKE HOW WE CAN'T STAND BEING IN SUCH CLOSE PROXIMITY WITH ONE ANOTHER THIS LONG?

EXACTLY.

THIS PROBABLY JUST GOES TO SHOW SOMETHING, BUT I SURE DON'T KNOW WHAT.

THERE'S QUITE A BREEZE UP HERE. I'M REALLY MOVING. THERE'S THE RIVER AND THE TOWN TRIANGLE.

HEY, DOWN THERE! MY NAME IS CALVIN! TELL MY TIGER, HOBBES, I'M BLOWING AWAY ON A BALLOON!

CAN ANYONE HEAR ME? TELL HOBBES HE CAN'T READ MY COMIC BOOKS JUST 'CAUSE I'M NOT AROUND, OK?

..OH, YEAH, TELL MY PARENTS WHAT HAPPENED, TOO, ALL RIGHT? HELLO? HELLO?

UH OH, I'M HEADING INTO A FLOCK OF DUCKS!

EXCUSE ME! COMING THROUGH!

PARDON ME! GANGWAY! BEEP BEEP!

..BOY, IF LOOKS COULD KILL.

MY HANDS ARE GETTING TIRED. I'LL TIE THE BALLOON STRING ONTO MY BELT LOOP.

THERE...

WHOOP

SHOOF

IF A PLANE COMES ALONG NOW, I'M GONNA DIE.

WELL, I SUPPOSE THINGS DON'T GET WORSE THAN HANGING FROM A HELIUM BALLOON A MILE ABOVE SOME UNRECOGNIZED STATE.

OF COURSE, MY GRIP COULD WEAKEN, OR I COULD GET SUCKED INTO A JET INTAKE.

THAT'S ONE OF THE REMARKABLE THINGS ABOUT LIFE. IT'S NEVER SO BAD THAT IT CAN'T GET WORSE.

BOY, I'M JUST GOING HIGHER AND HIGHER.

I SUPPOSE EVENTUALLY THE PRESSURE IN THE BALLOON WILL BE GREATER THAN THE AIR PRESSURE AROUND IT, AND THE BALLOON WILL...

POP!

THIS HAS GOT TO BE A DREAM.

WHENEVER YOU FALL FROM TWO MILES UP IN THE SKY, YOU LOOK DOWN, GASP, AND SUDDENLY WAKE UP.

GASP!

GASP
GASP
GASP
GASP
GASP

I WONDER IF MY LIFE WILL FLASH BEFORE MY EYES.

THAT'S THE PROBLEM WITH BEING SIX YEARS OLD...

...MY LIFE WON'T TAKE VERY LONG TO WATCH.

MAYBE I CAN GET A FEW SLOW-MOTION REPLAYS OF THE TIME I SMACKED SUSIE UPSIDE THE HEAD WITH A SLUSHBALL.

SAY, I WONDER IF I HAVE ANY GUM IN MY POCKET. I COULD BLOW A BIG BUBBLE, AND...

NOPE, NO GUM. LET'S TRY *THIS* POCKET.

MY TRANSMOGRIFIER GUN!!

BOY, THESE THINGS COME IN HANDY ALL THE TIME.

I FORGOT ALL ABOUT MY TRANSMOGRIFIER GUN! NOW I HAVE NOTHING TO WORRY ABOUT!

I'LL JUST POINT IT AT MYSELF AND TRANSMOGRIFY! I'M SAFE!

ZAP

WHERE HAVE YOU BEEN?? I'VE BEEN CALLING AND CALLING. YOUR DINNER'S COLD, I'M SURE.

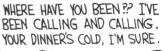

I DRIFTED AWAY ON MY BALLOON AND IT POPPED, BUT FORTUNATELY I HAD MY TRANSMOGRIFIER, SO AFTER I MISTAKENLY TURNED MYSELF INTO A SAFE, I TRANSMOGRIFIED INTO A LIGHT PARTICLE AND ZIPPED BACK HOME INSTANTANEOUSLY!

...OF COURSE, IF I'D KNOWN WE WERE HAVING **THIS**, I WOULDN'T HAVE HURRIED.

SOMETIME YOU SHOULD TRY TRANSMOGRIFYING YOURSELF INTO SOMEONE WHO OCCASIONALLY MAKES AN OUNCE OF SENSE.

Calvin and Hobbes
by WATTERSON

HERE'S "HAMSTER HUEY AND THE GOOEY KABLOOIE." YOU MIGHT LIKE THIS STORY.

YEAH? HOW GOOD CAN IT BE IF IT HASN'T BEEN MADE INTO AN ANIMATED TV SHOW?

I HOPE TONIGHT'S STORY ISN'T AS BORING AS *LAST* NIGHT'S WAS. IT PUT ME RIGHT TO SLEEP.

DON'T WORRY. *THIS* STORY WILL KEEP YOU UP ALL NIGHT.

REALLY? WHAT IS IT?

IT'S CALLED, "THE DISEMBODIED HAND THAT STRANGLED PEOPLE."

GOSH, THIS IS GREAT! HOW CREEPY! I *NEVER* GET A SCARY STORY! A DISEMBODIED HAND! WOW!

AND YOU KNOW WHAT'S *REALLY* SCARY? THEY NEVER FOUND IT! TO THIS DAY, NOBODY KNOWS WHERE THE HAND IS!

IN FACT, THE HAND COULD... OH NO!! THERE IT IS!

IT'S G-GOT ME!! GAKK!!

"CALVIN?... ...CALVIN?..

I SHOULD'VE THOUGHT OF THAT YEARS AGO.

CALVIN AND HOBBES
by WATTERSON

SPACEMAN SPIFF EXPLORES THE OUTERMOST REACHES OF THE UNIVERSE.

BY POPULAR REQUEST.

INTREPID EXPLORER SPACEMAN SPIFF LANDS ON AN UNCHARTED PLANET. WHAT STRANGE WONDERS WILL HE DISCOVER HERE?

SPIFF SETS OUT IN SEARCH OF SENTIENT LIFE!

WHAT A STRANGE PLANET THIS IS! ITS SURFACE IS SURPRISINGLY SOFT AND POROUS!

AND HERE CURIOUS GEYSERS BLAST HOT AIR!

SUDDENLY IT DAWNS ON HIM! SPIFF IS NOT ON THE PLANET'S SURFACE AT ALL! HE'S WALKING ON A RECLINING ALIEN!!

OUR HERO SETS HIS DEATH RAY BLASTER.

ZZ.. MMF HM?

LET'S GO, CALVIN! WE'RE ALL READY!

BOY, I HAVEN'T BEEN TO THE ZOO IN AGES.

AND CALVIN'S NEVER BEEN. THIS WILL BE FUN.

I'VE BEEN TELLING HIM ABOUT IT ALL WEEK. HE'S SO EXCITED.

C'MON, CALVIN!

SO *WHERE* DO WE HAVE TO GO NOW?

BEATS *ME*. MOM AND DAD ARE ALWAYS DRAGGING US *SOME* DUMB PLACE.

HOW COME THE ALLIGATORS ARE IN THIS BIG PIT?

SO THEY DON'T GET OUT AND EAT PEOPLE.

DOES THE ZOO EVER THROW ANYONE IN?

DON'T BE SILLY. OF COURSE NOT.

HOW SOON UNTIL WE GO HOME?

LOOK! MONKEYS!

SEE HOW THEY USE THEIR TAILS AND FEET TO CLIMB?

ZOOS LET PEOPLE SEE HOW WILD ANIMALS REALLY BEHAVE.

HEY, LOOK WHAT *THAT* MONKEY'S DOING! RIGHT IN PUBLIC, TOO! HA HA! THAT'S GROSS! HOW COME *I'M* NOT ALLOWED TO DO THAT?!

COME LOOK AT THE BIRDS OVER HERE, CALVIN.

WHAT DO YOU THINK OF THE ZOO?

I THINK IT'S KIND OF DEPRESSING.

I ALWAYS FEEL SORRY FOR THE ANIMALS. THEY DON'T HAVE MUCH ROOM TO MOVE, OR ANYTHING TO DO.

THEY JUST SLEEP UNTIL THEY'RE FED.

THAT'S PRETTY MUCH ALL *YOU* DO.

YOU KNOW WHAT I MEAN.

HEY, THOSE KIDS ARE FEEDING THE ANIMALS!

MOM, CAN I GET SOME PEANUTS TO FEED THE ANIMALS?

I'M NOT YOUR MOM.

WHOOP!

ARE YOU LOST? WHAT DOES YOUR MOM LOOK LIKE?

FROM THE KNEES DOWN, SHE LOOKS JUST LIKE YOU.

GOSH, I FOLLOWED THAT LADY HALFWAY AROUND THE ZOO, THINKING SHE WAS MY MOM.

WHY DON'T MOMS WRITE THEIR NAMES ON THEIR CALVES SO THIS KIND OF THING WOULDN'T HAPPEN?

I WONDER WHERE I AM. AND WHERE'S HOBBES? I THOUGHT HE WAS RIGHT WITH ME.

UH OH. WHERE'S CALVIN?

WHY DO THESE LITTLE FAMILY TRIPS ALWAYS TURN OUT THIS WAY? I'M GOING TO SPEND MORE SATURDAYS AT THE OFFICE.

I GOT A HIT!

SAFE!

OK, THAT WAS A SINGLE. I HAVE A GHOST RUNNER HERE NOW, SO I CAN BAT AGAIN.

AND MY GHOST RUNNERS WHO *WERE* ON FIRST AND SECOND BASE ARE NOW ON SECOND AND THIRD, RIGHT?

NOPE. THEY'RE BOTH OUT.

OUT?!

MY GHOST OUTFIELDER TAGGED YOUR GHOST GOING TO THIRD, AND THREW TO MY GHOST SECOND BASEMAN. IT WAS A BRILLIANT DOUBLE PLAY.

THAT NEVER HAPPENED!

YOU'VE GOT TWO OUTS.

WELL, MY GHOST ON FIRST JUST STOLE HOME, SO I'VE GOT ANOTHER RUN! HA HA, SMARTY!

YEAH, WELL, ALL MY OUTFIELD GHOSTS JUST RAN IN AND BEAT THE TOBACCO JUICE OUT OF HIM.

HA! THE GHOST UMPIRE JUST SUSPENDED ALL YOUR GHOSTS FOR ETERNITY. THEY'RE OUT OF THE GAME.

HMPH! IF MY GHOSTS DON'T PLAY, *I* DON'T PLAY.

YOU FORFEIT THE GAME THEN! YOU LOSE AUTOMATICALLY IF YOU QUIT!

THE GHOST CROWD SUPPORTS ME. THEY'RE "BOO"-ING YOU!

SOMETIMES I WISH I LIVED IN A NEIGHBORHOOD WITH MORE KIDS.

CALVIN and HOBBES by WATTERSON

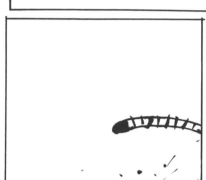

WE TIGERS JUST *LIVE* FOR THAT!

NOT FOR LONG, YOU WON'T.

Calvin and Hobbes

by Watterson

BOY, WHAT A BEAUTIFUL SUMMER MORNING, HUH, DAD? TOO BAD YOU CAN'T STAY HOME TO ENJOY IT.

WHEN YOU'RE OLD, YOU'LL BE SORRY YOU NEVER TOOK ADVANTAGE OF DAYS LIKE THESE, BUT OF COURSE, THAT'S FAR OFF, AND IN THE MEANTIME, THERE'S LOTS OF WORK TO BE DONE.

YEP, YOU'D BETTER GO TO WORK. HAVE A GOOD LONG DRIVE IN TRAFFIC. MAYBE YOU'LL GET HOME IN TIME TO WATCH THE SUN SET... IF YOU CAN STAY AWAKE. SO LONG!

GOLLY, I'D HATE TO HAVE A KID LIKE ME.

WHAT WOULD YOU DO IF I CREAMED YOU WITH THIS WATER BALLOON RIGHT NOW?

TAKE THE WORST THING YOU CAN IMAGINE, AND IMAGINE SOMETHING A HUNDRED TIMES WORSE THAN THAT.

YOU'D DO *THAT*?

NO, I'D DO SOMETHING EVEN WORSE.

HE PIQUED MY CURIOSITY.

BIP

WHEEEE.

77

WHAT ARE YOU DOING WITH ALL YOUR DAD'S TOOLS IN THE BATHROOM?

THIS FAUCET DRIPS, SO I'M GOING TO FIX IT.

YOU'RE GOING TO FIX IT?

THAT'S WHAT I SAID.

..AND YOU CAN KEEP YOUR COMMENTS TO YOURSELF, DR. DOOM.

I DIDN'T SAY ANYTHING.

FIXING A FAUCET IS EASY. ALL YOU DO IS TAKE IT APART, SEE WHAT'S LEAKING, PLUG IT UP, AND PUT IT BACK TOGETHER.

DOES YOUR MOM KNOW YOU'RE DOING THIS?

NOPE. IT'S GOING TO BE A SURPRISE.

AND WE ALL KNOW HOW SHE LOVES SURPRISES.

I CAN'T GET THIS HANDLE OFF. PASS ME THE HACK-SAW, WILL YOU?

AREN'T YOU SUPPOSED TO TURN THE WATER OFF BEFORE YOU TAKE APART A FAUCET?

THAT'S THE PROBLEM I'M TRYING TO FIX, YOU MORON! I CAN'T TURN THE WATER OFF BECAUSE THE FAUCET LEAKS!

SHEESH, WHERE WERE *YOU* WHEN THEY WERE PASSING OUT BRAINS?

OH NO! AUGHH! ACKK!

I'LL GET YOU SOME PAPER AND CARBONS FOR YOUR WRITTEN APOLOGY.

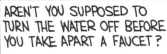

HOBBES, QUICK! HOW DO YOU TURN OFF THE WATER ?!? — HOW SHOULD **I** KNOW ??

I CAN'T PUT THIS PIECE BACK IN WITH ALL THIS WATER COMING OUT! — I'LL GET YOUR MOM!

MY MOM? HAVE YOU LOST YOUR MIND?? SHE CAN'T FIND OUT ABOUT THIS!

I'LL BET SHE NOTICES WHEN THE KITCHEN CEILING STARTS TO DRIP. — OPEN THE MEDICINE CABINET! FIND SOME CYANIDE!

♪ LA DA DEE DEE DA I THINK I'LL GET A BUCKET... DUM DE DOO.. ♪

♪♪ NOTHING'S WRONG...DA DEE DOO BA... I JUST WANT A BUCKET TO HOLD SOME...STUFF. TA TUM TA TUM ♪

LET'S SEE, HOW MANY BUCKETS DO WE HAVE? DUM DE DOO ♪ NO CAUSE FOR ALARM... NO NEED TO PANIC ... I JUST WANT A FEW BUCKETS. LA LA.

YOUR TURN.

CALVIN, WHAT ARE YOU DOING?

I'M... UH... GOING TO THE BATHROOM. — **FLUSH**

IS EVERYTHING ALL RIGHT?

FINE! DON'T COME UP! — **FLUSH**

WHAT'S ALL THAT WATER I HEAR? I'M COMING IN!

OH MY GOSH! ACKPBT! WHAT'S GOING ON?!? SPLUTB! BPLPTH!

THERE! I GOT THE WATER OFF. **ALL RIGHT, CALVIN, WHERE ARE YOU?!**

H-HI, DAD.

IT'S THE END OF THE WORLD, CALVIN.

LOOK AT THIS BATHROOM! WHAT ON EARTH WERE YOU *DOING?!*

NOTHING, DAD! I WAS JUST IN HERE LOOKING FOR SOME DENTAL FLOSS, WHEN *PLOOIE!* THE FAUCET HANDLE BLOWS SKY HIGH ALL BY ITSELF! IT... IT... UH...

WHAT I MEAN IS, HOBBES WAS FOOLING AROUND WITH YOUR TOOLS. I TRIED TO STOP HIM, BUT HE WOULDN'T LISTEN, AND SURE ENOUGH, HE WENT AND... AND...

ONE MORE TRY.

ALIENS, DAD! BIG, EVIL, BUG-EYED MONSTERS FROM PLUTO! THEY DID IT, AND MADE ME SWEAR NOT TO TELL!

BOY, DAD SURE BLEW HIS STACK *THAT* TIME, DIDN'T HE? WHAT A SOREHEAD!

LISTENING TO *HIM*, YOU'D THINK NOBODY IN THE WORLD HAD EVER NEEDED TO CALL A PLUMBER BEFORE. DAD'S GOT A JOB. HE CAN AFFORD IT.

DAD MAKES SUCH A BIG DEAL OUT OF EVERYTHING.

WHEN HE DOES, I SURE WISH YOU'D STOP TRYING TO PIN YOUR CRIMES ON *ME*.

OH, NOW *YOU'RE* GOING TO START IN ON ME *TOO*, HUH?

CALVIN and HOBBES
by WATTERSON

DINOSAURS EVERYWHERE FLEE FOR THEIR LIVES!

CALVIN IS COMING!

THE LATE CRETACEOUS: THE LAST EPOCH OF THE MIGHTY DINOSAURS!

KING OF THE THUNDER LIZARDS IS THE FEARSOME CALVIN, THE TYRANNOSAURUS!

SEVEN TONS OF MUSCLE AND TEETH. HE SEARCHES FOR PREY!

CALVIN, FOR GOODNESS' SAKE, STOP STOMPING AROUND! YOU'RE DRIVING ME CRAZY!

CHOMP!

HOW DID THE FEARSOME TYRANNOSAURUS BECOME EXTINCT? NOW WE KNOW!

WATTERSON

EVERYTHING FLOATS RANDOMLY IN THE ROOM! THERE'S NO GRAVITY!

CALVIN PUSHES OFF THE CEILING AT A SHARP ANGLE, AIMING FOR THE HALLWAY!

HE GLIDES WITH UNCHECKED MOMENTUM, TURNING HIM-SELF TO BE ABLE TO PUSH OFF THE NEXT STATIONARY SURFACE.

C'MON, YOU! OUTSIDE! YOU'RE REALLY BOUNCING OFF THE WALLS TODAY.

AW, MOM.

EXTRA PANTS...

THREE SHIRTS, TWO SWEATERS, TWO SWEATSHIRTS...

ANOTHER PAIR OF PANTS...

STILL TRYING TO LEARN TO RIDE THAT BICYCLE, EH?

I DON'T NEED ANY COMMENTS FROM YOU.

A SHADOW FALLS OVER THE LARGE CITY SKYSCRAPERS!

IT'S A GIGANTIC ANT! WITH ONE FOOTSTEP, IT PULVER-IZES THE ENTIRE DOWNTOWN! MILLIONS DIE INSTANTLY!

THE ANT BRUSHES THE CITY OFF THE MAP! PEOPLE FLOOD THE STREETS IN PANIC, ONLY TO BE SMASHED IN THE HORRIBLE WRECKAGE!

WELL... MAYBE I WON'T...

PLANET CALVIN MOVES ACROSS THE SOLAR SYSTEM.

NOBODY NOTICES UNTIL HIS ORBIT TAKES HIM DIRECTLY BETWEEN THE SUN AND EARTH.

CALVIN CAUSES A TOTAL SOLAR ECLIPSE! EARTH IS SHROUDED IN DARKNESS. HOW LONG WILL CALVIN STAY THERE?!

COULD YOU MOVE, PLEASE? YOU'RE IN MY LIGHT.

HA HA HAAA!

ELECTION DAY IS COMING UP. HAVE YOU DECIDED ON A RUNNING MATE?

A RUNNING MATE?

SURE. YOU CAN'T BE ELECTED DAD WITHOUT A MOM, RIGHT?

ARE YOU GOING TO KEEP THE MOM I'VE HAD, OR GET A NEW RUNNING MATE?

GEE...

BEDTIME, CALVIN.

OF COURSE I'LL STICK WITH YOUR MOM.

AWW...

ALL RIGHT, ALL RIGHT! I'M *GOING!*

HEY! LEGGO! I CAN WALK MYSELF! I JUST HAVE TO... *OK!* LOOK, I'M GOING! I'M GOING!

SURE, YOU THINK SCHOOL'S GREAT *NOW*, BUT IN A COUPLE OF HOURS YOU'LL *MISS* ME! YOU'LL SEE!

THERE GOES CALVIN OFF TO SCHOOL. HE SURE PUT UP A FUSS.

WELL, HE'LL HAVE FUN ONCE HE GETS THERE.

SEE, HE'S EVEN RUNNING NOW. HE'S ALL EXCITED ABOUT...

HEY! CALVIN, THE BUS STOP IS *THAT* WAY! COME BACK HERE!

I CAN'T BELIEVE I'M HERE WAITING TO GO TO SCHOOL. WHAT HAPPENED TO SUMMER?

GOSH, I COULDN'T *WAIT* FOR TODAY! SOON WE'LL BE MAKING NEW FRIENDS, LEARNING ALL SORTS OF IMPORTANT THINGS, AND...

WHAT'S THE MATTER WITH *YOU*??

YOUR BANGS DO A GOOD JOB OF COVERING UP THE LOBOTOMY STITCHES.

I PLEDGE ALLEGIANCE...

TO QUEEN FRAGG... AND HER MIGHTY STATE OF HYSTERIA...

IT'S GOING TO BE A LONG YEAR.

Hey, Calvin, you're on my swing. Get lost.

I'M NOT SCARED OF YOU, MOE.

Oh no?

NOPE. YOU'RE SO DUMB YOU PROBABLY NEVER THOUGHT ABOUT HOW A SPARROW'S SMALLER SIZE AND GREATER MANEUVERABILITY IS AN ADVANTAGE IN FIGHTING OFF BIG CROWS.

Yeah?

PUNCH

THOSE TV NATURE PROGRAMS WILL BE THE DEATH OF ME YET.

YES, CALVIN?

MAY I BE EXCUSED, PLEASE?

AGAIN?

I HAVE TO GO. BAD.

ALL RIGHT.

THANK YOU.

WHAT ARE *YOU* DOING HOME?!

I HAD TO GO.

CALVIN and HOBBES
by WATTERSON

SCHOOL'S OUT! FREE AT LAST!

AND JUST SIX PRECIOUS HOURS BEFORE BED TO FORGET EVERYTHING I LEARNED TODAY.

I HATE COMING HOME FROM SCHOOL. I NEVER KNOW IF HOBBES IS WAITING TO POUNCE ON ME.

MAYBE I CAN STAND OFF TO THE SIDE HERE, AND PUSH THE DOOR OPEN WITH A STICK.

I'M HOME!

VAPOW!

WHAT DO YOU DO, WAIT UNTIL YOU SEE THE WHITES OF MY EYES?!?

BOY, YOU SHOULD'VE *SEEN* THEM! THEY WERE AS BIG AS DINNER PLATES! HOO HOO HOO!

HAVE YOU BEEN READING THE PAPERS? GROWN-UPS REALLY HAVE THE WORLD FOULED UP.

ACID RAIN, TOXIC WASTES, HOLES IN THE OZONE, SEWAGE IN THE OCEANS, AND ON AND ON!

THE ONLY BRIGHT SIDE TO ALL THIS IS THAT EVENTUALLY THERE MAY NOT BE A PIECE OF THE PLANET WORTH FIGHTING OVER.

YOU'RE PACKING?

YEP. GET YOUR TOOTHBRUSH, HOBBES. WE'RE OUTTA HERE.

IT'S AN OUTRAGE HOW GROWN-UPS HAVE POLLUTED THE EARTH! I REFUSE TO INHERIT A SPOILED PLANET! I'M *LEAVING*!

REALLY? WHERE TO??

YOU KNOW, SOMETIMES YOU'RE A REAL LOAD TO HAVE AROUND.

I WAS JUST *ASKING!*

HOW ABOUT MARS? WE COULD GO THERE TO AVOID EARTH'S POLLUTION.

YEAH! IF WE GO *NOW*, WE CAN CLAIM IT AND KEEP EVERYONE ELSE OFF IT.

OK, IT'S SETTLED. MARS IT IS.

YOU FINISH PACKING. I'LL GO GET THE WAGON.

WE'RE GOING IN THE WAGON?

OF COURSE! WHAT DID *YOU* WANT TO DO? FLAP YOUR ARMS?

I GUESS I HADN'T THOUGHT ABOUT THAT PART.

OBVIOUSLY.

SO LONG, MOM. HOBBES AND I ARE GOING TO MARS TO LIVE. EARTH IS TOO POLLUTED.

HAVE A GOOD TIME.

SAY GOODBYE TO DAD FOR US. IF I CAN FIND AN INTERPLANETARY POST OFFICE, I'LL WRITE YOU ONCE IN A WHILE AND...

CALVIN, DON'T STAND THERE WITH THE DOOR OPEN. YOU'RE LETTING IN BUGS. EITHER STAY IN OR GO OUTSIDE.

SHE DIDN'T SEEM TOO CHOKED UP ABOUT US GOING, DID SHE?

WE SHOULD'VE LEFT A LONG TIME AGO.

BLAST OFF!

DO YOU REALLY THINK WE'LL GET ENOUGH LIFT TO BREAK EARTH'S GRAVITY?

OF COURSE! YOU THINK I DIDN'T PLAN THIS OUT?! I THOUGHT OF EVERYTHING.

DID YOU THINK OF WHAT YOU'LL EAT ON OUR TRIP?

PACKING WAS *YOUR* JOB! DIDN'T YOU PACK US ANY *FOOD*??

I PACKED FOOD FOR *ME*...

WE DID IT! WE CLEARED EARTH'S ORBIT!

MARS, HERE WE COME!

ARE YOU SURE THIS IS THE WAY?

WHAT? DIDN'T YOU BRING THE MAP?!

WELL, THIS IS OUR NEW HOME. I GUESS WE SHOULD UNPACK AND SET UP CAMP.

COMIC BOOKS... COMIC BOOKS... TUNA... SOME CANDY BARS... MORE TUNA... TOOTHBRUSHES... A CAN OPENER... LOOKS LIKE WE'RE ALL SET.

WHAT'S THIS?

A NIGHT LIGHT. I THOUGHT IT MIGHT BE SCARY SLEEPING ON A NEW PLANET.

BOY, YOU THOUGHT OF EVERYTHING.

NOW WE HAVE TO FIND AN OUTLET.

YEP, MARS MAY BE A LITTLE DULL, BUT IT'S BETTER THAN EARTH.

CRUNCH CRUNCH

WE'VE GOT A WHOLE PLANET TO OURSELVES. BRAND NEW AND UNSPOILED. NO PEOPLE, NO POLLUTION.

NOTHING BUT RUGGED, NATURAL BEAUTY AS FAR AS THE EYE CAN SEE.

THAT'S NOT YOUR CANDY BAR WRAPPER OVER THERE, IS IT?

IT WAS JUST THERE A MINUTE! I WASN'T GOING TO LEAVE IT.

I DON'T KNOW ABOUT YOU, BUT I LIKE IT HERE ON MARS.

I DO TOO. IT'S VERY PEACEFUL.

NOT ONLY THAT, BUT WE DON'T HAVE MOM HERE TO BOSS US AROUND! NO EARLY BEDTIME, NO BATHS, NO DISGUSTING DINNERS, NO...

DID THAT ROCK JUST MOVE?‽

MOMMMMM.‼

OH MY GOSH, THAT ROCK MOVED! THERE'S SOMETHING UNDER IT!

IT MUST BE A MARTIAN! OH NO! OH NO! IT'S PROBABLY SOME CREEPY, TENTACLED, BUG-EYED MONSTER!

YOU'RE RIGHT! THERE'S A TENTACLE NOW!

IT'S COMING OUT! WHAT WILL WE DO?!

AAUGHHHH!

IS THE MARTIAN STILL OUT THERE?

I'LL TAKE A PEEK.

I DON'T SEE HIM. HE MUST HAVE HIDDEN.

HIDDEN?? DO YOU THINK HE'S SCARED OF US?

WHY NOT? WE'RE SCARED OF HIM.

YEAH, BUT WE'RE JUST ORDINARY EARTHLINGS, NOT WEIRDOS FROM ANOTHER PLANET, LIKE HE IS.

WHY DO YOU THINK THE MARTIAN HID FROM US?

MAYBE MARTIANS DON'T LIKE EARTHLINGS.

DON'T LIKE US?! WHAT'S NOT TO LIKE?? THERE'S NOTHING WRONG WITH HUMANS!

HEY, YOU MARTIAN! COME ON OUT! WE'RE NOT BAD! WE JUST CAME HERE BECAUSE PEOPLE POLLUTED OUR OWN PLANET SO MUCH THAT... UH.. WHAT I MEAN, IS... UM...

SO WHAT ARE YOU SAYING? THAT OUR REPUTATION PRECEDED US?

WOULD YOU WELCOME IN A DOG THAT WASN'T HOUSE-TRAINED?

Panel 1:
I GUESS WE SHOULD GO HOME TO EARTH.

YEAH, WE MAY NOT BE WELCOME HERE.

Panel 2:
WE OUGHT TO FIX UP OUR OWN PLANET BEFORE WE GO MESSING AROUND WITH OTHER PEOPLE'S PLANETS.

Panel 3:
AFTER ALL, THERE'S ONLY ONE EARTH, AND IT'S GOT TO LAST US A WHILE.

Panel 4:
WE ALSO SHOULD GO HOME BECAUSE WE'RE CLEAN OUT OF TUNA.

I HOPE MOM AND DAD DIDN'T RENT OUT MY ROOM.

Panel 5:
THERE'S EARTH! WE'RE ALMOST HOME!

Panel 6:
LOOK, YOU CAN SEE THE CONTINENTS.

Panel 7:
HMM... IF I REMEMBER MY ATLAS, WE LIVE IN A BIG, PURPLE COUNTRY.

AND OUR HOUSE IS BY THE GIANT LETTER "E" IN THE WORD "STATES".

Panel 8:
HI, DAD! GUESS WHAT HOBBES AND I DID! WE WENT TO MARS!

WELL, WELL.

Panel 9:
YEP. WE WERE GOING TO LIVE THERE BECAUSE EARTH IS SO POLLUTED, BUT WE DISCOVERED THAT MARS IS INHABITED, SO WE CAME BACK HOME.

Panel 10:
YOU DIDN'T LIKE THE MARTIANS?

NO, THEY DIDN'T LIKE *US*. I THINK THEY WERE AFRAID WE'D JUNK UP MARS THE WAY WE'VE JUNKED UP EARTH.

Panel 11:
WHAT'S MY GOOD BRIEFCASE DOING OUT, AND WHY DOES IT SMELL LIKE TUNA FISH?!

AND CAN YOU BELIEVE IT, DAD? WE GO CLEAR TO MARS, AND DUMB OL' HOBBES FORGETS THE CAMERA!

Calvin and HOBBES
by WATTERSON
CALL IT.
TAILS.
OK, BEST TWO OUT OF THREE.
OOOMPH
LET'S CHANGE THIS TO TOUCH FOOTBALL, OK?
WATTERSON

FOR SHOW AND TELL, I BROUGHT A SPACE ALIEN I CAPTURED IN MY BACK YARD.

YES, FOR THE LAST TWO DAYS I'VE BEEN KEEPING IT IN THIS SPECIAL ZARNIUM-COATED BAG, AND FEEDING IT PURE AMMONIA!

AND NOW, THE MOMENT YOU'VE ALL BEEN WAITING FOR!

AARGH

HOW'D IT WORK?

MY TEACHER SAYS MOM AND DAD BOTH HAVE TO SIGN MY REPORT CARDS THIS YEAR.

SCOOTCH SCOOTCH

GREETINGS. I AM AN X-387 ROBOT PROBE SENT FROM JUPITER.

MM HMM.

MY SENSORS INDICATE TRACE AMOUNTS OF CHOCOLATE IN THE PANTRY. PLEASE LOAD SOME IN MY SCOOP FOR ANALYSIS.

NO, YOU'LL SPOIL YOUR APPETITE.

MY MISSION MUST NOT FAIL. PREPARE FOR ANNIHILATION, PITIFUL EARTH FEMALE.

GO BACK TO JUPITER, X-3 WHATEVER.

YOU KNOW, WHEN YOU THINK ABOUT IT, OUR LIVES ARE PRETTY NICE.

A LOT OF KIDS DON'T HAVE AS GOOD OF A HOME LIFE AS WE DO. WE REALLY CAN'T COMPLAIN.

..WHICH ISN'T TO SAY WE SHOULD GO HOME YET.

WHEN DO YOU THINK THEY'LL SEE THE CAR WINDSHIELD?

I THINK THE WORST OF THIS IS OVER, SO JUST TRY TO GET SOME SLEEP.

I'M GOING BACK TO BED, BUT GIVE ME A CALL IF YOU FEEL SICK AGAIN, OK? NOW GET SOME REST.

MM HMM.

POOR LITTLE KID.

YECCHHH! THERE IS NOTHING WORSE THAN A SICK ROOM-MATE! FACE THAT WAY!

Z

IT'S SCARY BEING SICK... ESPECIALLY AT NIGHT.

WHAT IF SOMETHING IS REALLY WRONG WITH ME, AND I HAVE TO GO TO THE HOSPITAL??

WHAT IF THEY STICK ME FULL OF TUBES AND HOSES? WHAT IF THEY HAVE TO OPERATE? WHAT IF THE OPERATION FAILS? WHAT IF THIS IS MY... MY... LAST NIGHT... ALIVE??

THEN I CAN LOOK FORWARD TO HAVING THE BED TO MYSELF TOMORROW.

FEW THINGS ARE LESS COMFORTING THAN A TIGER WHO'S UP TOO LATE.

FEELING ANY BETTER THIS MORNING, CALVIN?

NO.

I GUESS I'D BETTER MAKE YOU AN APPOINTMENT WITH THE DOCTOR.

OK.

IT'S SATURDAY, BY THE WAY. YOU WON'T MISS SCHOOL.

I KNOW.

Panel 1: WELL, IT LOOKS LIKE CALVIN JUST CAUGHT THE BUG GOING AROUND. NOTHING SERIOUS.

Panel 2: KEEP AN EYE ON HIM, AND LET ME KNOW IF HE ISN'T FEELING BETTER SOON.

OK. THANK YOU.

Panel 3: SO LONG, CALVIN. YOU WERE A GOOD PATIENT THIS TIME.

MM.

Panel 4: NOTHING LIKE A LITTLE VIRUS TO TAKE THE EDGE OFF A KID.

I'D STILL RATHER LET HIS TEACHER DEAL WITH HIM.

Panel 5: I GET TO STAY HOME FROM SCHOOL TODAY.

Panel 6: I GET TO LIE IN BED, DRINK TEA, AND READ COMIC BOOKS ALL DAY.

Panel 7: I WISH I COULD DO THIS EVERY DAY.

Panel 8: ...LIKE SOME PEOPLE I KNOW.

YOUR MOM DOESN'T BRING *ME* TEA IN BED.

Panel 9: I WANT SOME MORE TOAST.

Panel 10: ROOM SERVICE!!

Panel 11: HA! *THAT* SURE GOT YOU UP HERE QUICK!

TOMORROW YOU'RE GOING TO SCHOOL.

I THINK PEOPLE WORRY TOO MUCH ABOUT LITTLE THINGS.

ALL THEY DO IS MAKE THEMSELVES UNHAPPY THAT WAY.

WHY GET AN ULCER OVER THINGS THAT DON'T REALLY MATTER?

LIKE THE BOOK REPORT YOU'RE SUPPOSED TO BE WRITING NOW ON THE BOOK YOU HAVEN'T READ?

EXACTLY. CASE IN POINT.

WHY IN THE WORLD AM I WAITING IN THE POURING RAIN FOR THE SCHOOL BUS TO TAKE ME SOMEWHERE I DON'T EVEN WANT TO GO?

I GO TO SCHOOL, BUT I NEVER LEARN WHAT I WANT TO KNOW.

I HATE SCHOOL.

EACH DAY I COUNT THE HOURS UNTIL SCHOOL'S OVER. THEN I COUNT THE DAYS UNTIL THE WEEKEND. THEN I COUNT THE WEEKS UNTIL THE MONTH IS OVER, AND THEN THE MONTHS UNTIL SUMMER.

I ALWAYS HAVE TO POSTPONE WHAT I *WANT* TO DO FOR WHAT I *HAVE* TO DO!

WELCOME TO THE WORLD.

WOULD YOU SIGN THIS PARENTAL EXCUSE TO GET ME OUT OF THE NEXT 11½ YEARS OF SCHOOL?

Calvin and Hobbes by WATTERSON

THE VALIANT SPACEMAN SPIFF, INTERGALACTIC EXPLORER, COMES IN OVER THE MOUNTAINS OF A STRANGE PLANET!

OUR HERO DESPERATELY HOPES TO FIND A REST AREA WITH WORKING FACILITIES.

SPACEMAN SPIFF LANDS ON THE DISTANT PLANET ZOKK!

CLIMBING DOWN FROM HIS SPACECRAFT, OUR HERO PREPARES TO EXPLORE THE SURFACE!

UNEXPECTEDLY, SPIFF'S FIRST STEP SENDS HIM CAREENING THROUGH THE SKY!

SPIFF QUICKLY REALIZES THAT PLANET ZOKK HAS ONLY A FRACTION OF EARTH'S GRAVITY!

OOF

WITH PRACTICE, OUR HERO SOON FINDS HE CAN BOUND EFFORTLESSLY ACROSS THE LANDSCAPE!

STOP BOUNCING ON THE BED AND GO TO SLEEP!

DUMB BALLOON.

POOF POOF

POOF POOOF

POOFF

HEY, SUSIE, DID YOU HAVE ANY TROUBLE WITH OUR MATH HOMEWORK LAST NIGHT?

NO, WHY?

I THOUGHT A COUPLE OF THESE WERE TRICKY. CAN I CHECK MY ANSWERS WITH YOURS?

OK.

THANKS. WHAT DID YOU GET FOR QUESTION ONE?

SEVEN.

SEVEN? GOOD, THAT'S WHAT *I* GOT. WHAT DID YOU GET FOR QUESTION TWO?

DROP DEAD, CALVIN.

EVER SIT AND WATCH ANTS?

LOOK AT THIS ONE. HE'S CARRYING A CRUMB THAT'S BIGGER THAN HE IS, AND HE'S *RUNNING*.

AND IF YOU PUT AN OBSTACLE IN FRONT OF HIM, HE'LL SCRAMBLE LIKE CRAZY UNTIL HE GETS ACROSS IT. HE DOESN'T LET ANYTHING STOP HIM.

I JUST CAN'T IDENTIFY WITH THAT KIND OF WORK ETHIC.

Calvin and Hobbes

by WATTERSON

I FEEL A BIG SNEEZE WELLING UP.

...WHICH IS ALWAYS A SURE SIGN THAT I'M NOT CARRYING A HANDKERCHIEF.

AH...AH...AH..

CHOOOOO!

MOM, I SNEEZED AND BLEW MY HEAD OFF!

PULL YOUR SHIRT DOWN, CALVIN. YOU'RE NOT FOOLING ANYONE.

MOM WOULD BE A LOT MORE FUN IF SHE WAS A LITTLE MORE GULLIBLE.

JUST THINK, EARTH WAS A CLOUD OF DUST 4.5 BILLION YEARS AGO...

3 BILLION YEARS AGO, THE FIRST BACTERIA APPEARED. THEN CAME SEA LIFE, DINOSAURS, BIRDS, MAMMALS, AND, FINALLY, A MILLION YEARS AGO, MAN.

NOW IN 1988, THERE'S ME.

...THE ACME OF EVOLUTION.

OH, *PLEASE*.

IT'S NOT QUITE THE SAME, IS IT?

AND IT PROBABLY WON'T SNOW FOR ANOTHER MONTH AT LEAST.

Z Z

GRRR Z

GROWLL RRR!

PSST! HEY! WAKE UP! YOU'RE DREAMING!

GRRRR..

AND MOM WONDERS WHY I NEVER LOOK RESTED IN THE MORNING.

CALVIN, TAKE OFF YOUR OUTFIT BEFORE YOU SIT AT THE TABLE, OK?

CALVIN? WHO'S CALVIN? I'M *STUPENDOUS MAN!*

STOP BEING SILLY, AND DO AS I ASKED YOU.

BUT MOM, I *NEED* TO WEAR THIS FOR DINNER!

NO YOU DON'T. LET'S GO.

BUT STUPENDOUS MAN HAS A STOMACH OF STEEL!

MOM SAID I CAN'T GO OUTSIDE UNTIL I FINISH MY HOMEWORK. IF YOU'LL HELP ME, I'LL BE DONE FASTER. WHAT'S FIVE PLUS SEVEN?

I DON'T KNOW.

I DON'T EITHER.

THEN WRITE, "I DON'T KNOW."

HEY, THAT'S A TRUE ANSWER, ISN'T IT! I CAN WRITE THAT FOR *ALL* OF THESE! WE'RE DONE!

WE'D BETTER HAVE A LOOK AT OUR PRODIGY'S HOMEWORK.

WANT TO GO PLAY OUTSIDE?

NO. I'M WATCHING TV.

YOU HATE THIS SHOW. LET'S GO OUT.

NAH.

WHY NOT?

DAD FINALLY SAID HE WAS SICK OF ARGUING WITH ME, AND FOR ALL HE CARED, I COULD WATCH TV UNTIL MY BRAINS OOZED OUT MY EARS.

SO YOU'RE GOING TO?

IT WAS A HARD-WON PRIVILEGE.

CALVIN and HOBBES

by WATTERSON

FLAPS ....CHECK.
FUEL ....CHECK.
LANDING GEAR .... CHECK.

GOGGLES... CHECK.

CALVIN PILOTS HIS F-15 AT MORE THAN 1,500 MILES AN HOUR.

LOADED WITH TONS OF EVERY CONCEIVABLE MISSILE, THE JET SHRIEKS LOW OVER THE GROUND!

FWISSHHH!

UP AND OVER THE NEXT RISE, HIS TARGET COMES INTO VIEW! CALVIN *FIRES!*

MISSILE AFTER MISSILE STREAKS AHEAD AND DETONATES WITH GRIM ACCURACY!

PFOOM!

MISSION ACCOMPLISHED! A SMOLDERING CRATER IS ALL THAT REMAINS OF CALVIN'S ELEMENTARY SCHOOL!

ELEMENTARY SCHOOL

SIGH..

WELL DAD, WE'RE RIGHT DOWN TO THE WIRE, AND THE POLLS SAY YOU WON'T BE DAD HERE MUCH LONGER.

IT SEEMS YOU'RE JUST NOT LIKABLE ENOUGH. THOSE POLLED CONTINUE TO FIND YOU A COLD FISH.

IF YOU WANT SOME ADVICE, I'D SUGGEST YOU DO SOMETHING EXTRAORDINARILY LIKABLE IN THE NEXT TWO MINUTES.

GO TO BED.

NO, NO! IT'S *WAY* TOO LATE TO LEARN HOW TO TELL JOKES.

TEN... FIFTEEN ... SIX... TWENTY-TWO...

HIKE!

YAAAA

AUGH!

ANOTHER FIVE YARD LOSS!

WE'VE GOT TO GET SOME OTHER PLAYERS.

BOY, YOU'RE LUCKY *YOU* DON'T HAVE TO GO TO SCHOOL LIKE *I* DO.

YOU DON'T KNOW WHAT IT'S LIKE TO GET UP ON THESE COLD, DARK MORNINGS AND HAVE TO GO SOMEPLACE YOU HATE.

YES I DO.

OH YEAH? HOW COULD YOU?

YOU TELL ME EVERY MORNING.

OH, AM I KEEPING YOU AWAKE?! I'M *SORRY!*

RINGGG

HEY, SUSIE, CAN I BORROW YOUR BLACK CRAYON?

OK, BUT DON'T BREAK IT, AND DON'T PEEL THE PAPER OFF, AND COLOR WITH ALL SIDES OF IT SO IT STAYS POINTY.

GEEZ, WHY DON'T YOU TAKE OUT AN INSURANCE POLICY ON IT?

JUST DON'T RUIN MY CRAYON. WHAT ARE YOU DRAWING ANYWAY?

BLACK BEARS ATTACKING A BLACK FOREST CAMPGROUND AT MIDNIGHT.

GIVE ME MY CRAYON BACK.

HEY! WHAT'S THIS STUFF IN MY SOUP?! YECCHH! IS THIS RICE?!? IT HAD BETTER *NOT* BE!

RICE? LET ME SEE.

LOOK! THESE LITTLE WHITE THINGS! SEE, THERE'S RICE IN MY SOUP! I HATE RICE!

I DIDN'T PUT ANY RICE IN. THOSE ARE MAGGOTS.

EWWWW!

ANOTHER LOVELY MEAL AT HOME WITH MY FAMILY. ...I WISH MY JOB REQUIRED MORE TRAVEL.

WELL, HE'S *EATING* IT NOW, RIGHT?

GOSH, WAIT 'TIL I TELL EVERYONE AT SCHOOL WHAT *WE* HAD FOR DINNER!

UH OH.

HOOP

EEP!

I'VE GOT THE HICCUPS SOMETHING TERRIBLE, MOM.

DRINK SOME WATER.

BANG! I GOTCHA!

ARGG!

GAAACKK

UGHH!

HERE.

WHAT'S THIS?

IT'S YOUR DEATH RATTLE!

SHOOKA SHOOKA

IT MUST BE AWFUL TO BE A GIRL.

I'M SURE IT'S FRUSTRATING KNOWING THAT MEN ARE BIGGER, STRONGER AND BETTER AT ABSTRACT THOUGHT THAN WOMEN.

REALLY, IF YOU'RE A GIRL, WHAT WOULD MAKE YOU GO ON LIVING?

THE THOUGHT OF A JERK LIKE YOU BEGGING ONE OF US FOR A DATE WHEN YOU'RE 17.

HA! NOT *ME*! GROSS!

THE TYRANNOSAURUS STALKS THE CRETACEOUS SHORES!

THE 5-TON CARNIVOROUS LIZARD CAN RUN FASTER THAN A CHARGING RHINO! WHAT COULD BE MORE HORRIFYING?

STOP THAT CLOMPING AROUND!!

...BESIDES THE BLOOD-CURDLING ROAR OF ITS MOM...

WHEN I GROW UP, I WANT TO BE AN INVENTOR. FIRST I WILL INVENT A TIME MACHINE.

THEN I'LL COME BACK TO YESTERDAY

AND TAKE MYSELF TO TOMORROW

AND SKIP THIS DUMB ASSIGNMENT.

MOMMM, I'M HOME FROM SCHOOL! OPEN THE DOOR FOR ME, OK?

WHAT'S THE MATTER? IT WASN'T LOCKED.

SOMETIMES HOBBES IS WAITING TO POUNCE ON ME AS SOON AS I OPEN THE DOOR.

OH FOR HEAVEN'S SAKE! FROM NOW ON, DON'T CALL ME TO COME TO THE DOOR UNLESS IT'S LOCKED.

HA! I SURE OUT-SMARTED HOBBES *THIS* TIME!

THBBPTT!

SISSY.

BOY, I'M IN A BAD MOOD TODAY! EVERYONE HAD BETTER STEER CLEAR OF ME!

I HATE *EVERYBODY!* AS FAR AS I'M CONCERNED, EVERYONE ON THE PLANET CAN JUST DROP DEAD. PEOPLE ARE SCUM.

WELL-L-L? DOESN'T ANYONE WANT TO CHEER ME UP?!?

GET OUT OF MY WAY! I'M IN A BAD MOOD!

I'LL BET A PET DOG WOULD'VE GOTTEN OUT OF MY WAY.

WATCH OUT, MOM. I'M IN A BAD MOOD.

BE IN A BAD MOOD SOMEWHERE ELSE, OK? I'M BUSY.

HMPH! I'LL BET MY *BIOLOGICAL* MOTHER WOULD'VE BOUGHT ME A COMIC BOOK AND MADE ME FEEL BETTER INSTEAD OF SHUNNING ME LIKE *YOU*.

KID, ANYONE *BUT* YOUR BIOLOGICAL MOTHER WOULD'VE LEFT YOU TO THE WOLVES LONG AGO.

YEAH, RIGHT. REALLY, HOW MUCH DID YOU PAY FOR ME?

I WISH IT WOULD SNOW EIGHT FEET IN THE NEXT FIVE MINUTES SO THEY'D HAVE TO CLOSE SCHOOL.

C'MON, SNOW! SNOW SNOW SNOW SNOW SNOW SNOW SNOW SNOW!

SO CLOSE... AND YET SO FAR.

DO YOU THINK GOD LETS YOU PLEA BARGAIN?

I'D WORRY MORE ABOUT YOUR MOM.

HELLO?

HI, DAD! IT'S ME, CALVIN. WILL YOU TELL ME A STORY?

CALVIN, I'M AT WORK! I DON'T HAVE TIME TO TELL YOU A STORY NOW! I'M VERY BUSY! GET OFF THE PHONE. I'M EXPECTING IMPORTANT CALLS.

OK, DAD. I'LL JUST STAY HERE QUIETLY GROWING UP AT AN UNBELIEVABLE RATE, NEVER SPENDING MUCH SPECIAL TIME WITH MY OWN DAD, WHO'S ALWAYS WORKING.

RIGHT, RIGHT. THIS IS THE STORY OF THE HYDRAULIC PUMP (Fig.1), THE WHEEL SHAFT FLANGE (Fig.2), AND THE EVIL PATENT INFRINGEMENT.

I WANT A *GOOD* STORY.

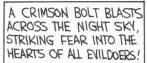

The End